This book belongs to:

Name _____

Address _____

_____

_____

A A MILNE

THE

POOH DIARY
FOR ANY YEAR

ILLUSTRATED by E.H.SHEPARD

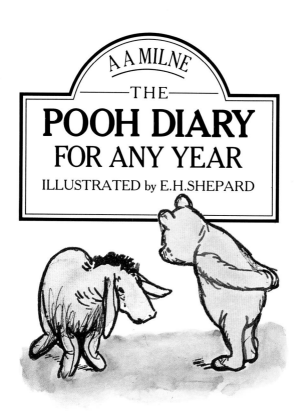

Methuen Children's Books

First published in 1990
by Methuen Children's Books
Reprinted 1991, 1992
Reprinted 1993 by Methuen Children's Books
an imprint of Reed Children's Books
Michelin House, 81 Fulham Road, London SW3 6RB
and Auckland, Melbourne, Singapore and Toronto

Printed in Italy by Olivotto

ISBN 0 416 16052 2

They all sang the Outdoor Song for Snowy Weather the
rest of the way home, Piglet, who was still not quite
sure of his voice, putting in the tiddely-poms again.

JANUARY

1   Barbara

2

3   Anne Robson.

4 _____

5 _____

6 _____

7 _____

_____

8 _____

_____

9 _____

_____

10 _____

11 _____

_____

_____

12 _____

_____

_____

The more it SNOWS-tiddely-pom . . .

The more it GOES-tiddely-pom On Snowing.

13 _____

_____

14 _____

_____

15 _____

_____

16 _____

_____

17 _____

_____

18 _____

_____

'We've finished our House!'
sang the gruff voice.
'Tiddely pom!' sang the squeaky one.
'It's a beautiful H O U S E . . .'
'Tiddely pom . . .'
'I wish it were M I N E . . .'
'Tiddely pom . . .'

19 _____

_____

20 _____

_____

21 _____

22 _____

_____

_____

23 _____

_____

_____

24 _____

_____

_____

25 _____

_____

_____

'Tracks,' said Piglet. 'Paw-marks.' He gave a little squeak of excitement. 'Oh, Pooh! Do you think it's a – a – a Woozle?'

26 _____

_____

_____

27 _____

_____

_____

28 _____

_____

_____

29 _____

_____

30 _____

_____

31 _____

_____

'It may be,' said Pooh. 'Sometimes it is, and
sometimes it isn't. You can never tell with paw-marks.'

'A lick of honey,' murmured Bear to himself, 'or – or not, as the case may be.' And he gave a deep sigh, and tried very hard to listen to what Owl was saying.

FEBRUARY

1 _____

_____

2 _____

_____

3 _____

_____

4 _____

5 _____

6 _____

7 _____

8 _____

9 _____

_____

10 _____

_____

11 _____

_____

12 _____

_____

13 _____

_____

14 _____

_____

15 _____

_____

16 _____

_____

17 _____

_____

Before he knew where he was, Piglet was in the bath,
and Kanga was scrubbing him firmly with a large
lathery flannel.

18 _____

_____

_____

19 _____

_____

_____

20 _____

_____

_____

21 _____

_____

_____

22 _____

_____

_____

23 _____

_____

_____

24 _____

_____

_____

25 _____

_____

26 _____

_____

27 _____

_____

28 _____

_____

29 _____

'Supposing a tree fell down, Pooh, when we were underneath it
'Supposing it didn't,' said Pooh after careful thought.

MARCH

1

2

3

4

_____

_____

5

_____

_____

6

_____

_____

7

_____

_____

The wind was against them now, and Piglet's ears streamed behind him . . .

8   . . . like banners

9

10

11

12

13

. . . as he fought his way along.

14

15

16

17

18 _____

_____

19 _____

_____

They all crashed together on to what had once been the floor,
but was now trying to see what it looked like as a wall.

20 _____

_____

_____

21 _____

_____

_____

'I have been told – the news has worked through to
my corner of the Forest – the damp bit down on the
right which nobody wants – that a certain Person is
looking for a house.'

22 _____

_____

23 _____

_____

24 _____

_____

25 _____

_____

26 _____

_____

Christopher Robin was telling them what to do, and Rabbit was telling them again directly afterwards, in case they hadn't heard.

27 _____

_____

_____

28 _____

_____

_____

29 _____

_____

Kanga was down below tying the
things on, and calling out to Owl,
'You won't want this dirty old dish-
cloth any more, will you, and what
about this carpet, it's all in holes.'

30 _____

_____

31 _____

_____

Christopher Robin lived at the very top of the Forest. It rained, and it rained, and it rained, but the water couldn't come up to *his* house.

Every morning he went out with his umbrella and put a stick in the place where the water came up to, and every next morning he went out and couldn't see his stick any more, so he put another stick in the place where the water came up to.

APRIL

1 _____

_____

2 _____

_____

3 _____

_____

4 _____

_____

_____

5 _____

_____

6 _____

_____

7 _____

_____

8 _____

_____

9 _Me!_ _____

_____

_____

10 _____

_____

_____

11 _____

_____

_____

12 _____

_____

_____

13 _____

_____

14 _____

_____

_____

15 Sharon _____

_____

16 _____

_____

17 _____

_____

18 _____

_____

19 _____

_____

20 _____

_____

21 _____

_____

'We might go in your umbrella,' said Pooh.

22 _____

_____

23 _____

_____

24 _____

_____

25 _____

_____

26 _____

_____

27 _____

_____

28 _____

_____

29 _____

_____

_____

30 _____

_____

So Winnie-the-Pooh went round to his friend
Christopher Robin, who lived behind a green door in
another part of the Forest.

MAY

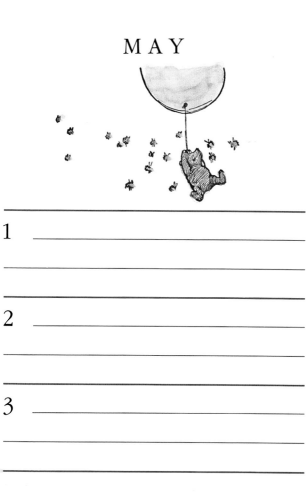

1 _____

_____

2 _____

_____

3 _____

_____

How sweet to be a Cloud
Floating in the Blue!
Every little cloud
Always sings aloud.

4 _____

_____

_____

5 _____

_____

_____

6 _____

_____

_____

7 _____

_____

_____

8 _____

_____

9 _____

_____

10 _____

_____

11 _____

_____

_____

12 _____

_____

13 _____

_____

14 _____

_____

15 _____

_____

Isn't it funny
How a bear likes honey?
Buzz! Buzz! Buzz!
I wonder why he does?

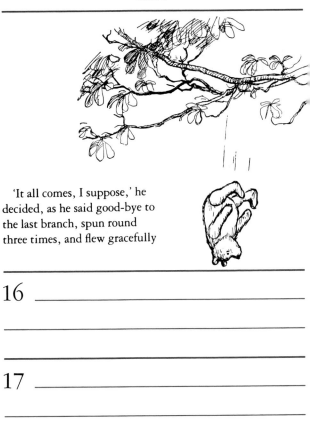

'It all comes, I suppose,' he decided, as he said good-bye to the last branch, spun round three times, and flew gracefully

16 _____

_____

17 _____

_____

18 _____

_____

_____

19 _____

_____

_____

20 _____

_____

_____

21 _____

_____

_____

into a gorse-bush, 'it all comes of *liking* honey so much.'

22 _____

_____

_____

23 _____

_____

_____

24 _____

_____

But his arms were so stiff from holding on to the string
of the balloon all that time that they stayed up straight
in the air for more than a week, and whenever a fly came
and settled on his nose he had to blow it off. And I think
– but I am not sure – that *that* is why he was always
called Pooh.

25 _____

26 _____

27 _____

28 _____

29 _____

_____

_____

30 _____

_____

_____

31 _____

_____

Well, he was humming this hum to himself, and walking gaily along, wondering what everybody else was doing, and what it felt like, being somebody else.

JUNE

1 _____

_____

2 _____

_____

3 _____

_____

4 _____

_____

5 _____

_____

6 _____

_____

7 _____

_____

8 _____

_____

9 _____

_____

10 _____

_____

11 _____

_____

12 _____

_____

13 _____

_____

14 _____

_____

15 _____

_____

16 _____

_____

17 _____

_____

18 _____

_____

'Then would you read a Sustaining Book, such as
would help and comfort a Wedged Bear in Great
Tightness?'

19 _____

_____

20 _____

_____

21 _____

_____

22 _____

_____

23 _____

_____

24 _____

_____

25 _____

_____

26 _____

_____

27 _____

_____

28 _____

_____

29 _____

_____

30 _____

_____

For a long time they looked at the river beneath them,
saying nothing, and the river said nothing too, for it felt
very quiet and peaceful on this summer afternoon.

J U L Y

1 _____

_____

2 _____

_____

3 _____

_____

'Supposing we hit him by mistake?'
said Piglet anxiously.
Pooh dropped his stone.

4 _____

_____

5 _____

_____

6 _____

_____

7 _____

_____

8 _____

_____

9 _____

_____

10 _____

_____

There was a loud splash, and Eeyore disappeared. . . .

11 _____

_____

_____

12 _____

_____

_____

13 _____

_____

Here it comes!
A very – big – grey –
Oh, no, it isn't,
it's Eeyore.

14

'Oh, Eeyore, you *are* wet!' said Piglet, feeling him.
Eeyore shook himself, and asked somebody to explain to
Piglet what happened when you had been inside a river
for quite a long time.

15 _____

_____

_____

16 _____

_____

_____

17 _____

_____

_____

18 _____

_____

_____

19 _____

_____

_____

'Somebody BOUNCED me. I was just thinking by
the side of the river – thinking, if any of you know what
that means – when I received a loud BOUNCE.'

20 _____

_____

21 _____

_____

22 _____

_____

23 _____

_____

24 _____

_____

Christopher Robin came down from the Forest to the
bridge, feeling all sunny and careless.

25 _____

_____

26 _____

_____

27 _____

_____

28 _____

_____

_____

_____

29 ———————————

30 ———————————

31 ———————————

Poor Eeyore is in a Very Sad Condition, because it's his birthday, and nobody has taken any notice of it, and he's very Gloomy – you know what Eeyore is . . .

AUGUST

1 _____

_____

2 _____

_____

3 _____

_____

4 _____

_____

_____

5 _____

_____

6 _____

_____

7 _____

_____

8 _____

_____

_____

9 _____

_____

10 _____

_____

11 _____

_____

12 _____

_____

Piglet had gone back to his own
house to get Eeyore's balloon . . . and
he ran as fast as he could so as to get
to Eeyore before Pooh did.

13

14

15

16

BANG!!!???***!!!
Piglet lay there, wondering
what had happened.

'Hallo, Pooh,' said Piglet.
'What are *you* trying to do?'
'I was trying to reach the knocker,' said Piglet.
'I just came round—'

'Here it is. With – with many happy returns of the day.'
And he gave Eeyore the small piece of damp rag.

17 _____

_____

_____

18 _____

_____

_____

19 _____

_____

20 _____

_____

_____

21 _____

_____

_____

22 _____

_____

_____

23 _____

_____

_____   _____

24 Nigel

25

26

'This party,' said Christopher Robin, 'is a party
because of what someone did, and we all know who it
was, and it's his party, because of what he did.'

'For Pooh?' said Eeyore.

'Of course it is. The best bear in all the world.'

'I might have known,' said Eeyore. 'After all, one can't complain. I have my friends.'

27 _____

_____

28 _____

_____

29 _____

_____

30 _____

_____

31 _____

_____

Nobody was listening, for they were all saying, 'Open it, Pooh,' 'What is it, Pooh?' 'I know what it is,' 'No, you don't.'

They all said, 'Hallo,' and felt awkward and unhappy
suddenly, because it was a sort of good-bye they were
saying, and they didn't want to think about it.

SEPTEMBER

1 _____

2 _____

3 _____

4 _____

_____

5 _____

_____

6 _____

_____

7 _____

_____

8 _____

_____

9

10 Treva

11

12

13

14 _____

_____

_____

15 _____

_____

_____

'Christopher Robin, we've come to say – to give you – it's called – written by – but we've all – because we've heard, I mean we all know – well, you see, it's – we – you – well, that, to put it as shortly as possible, is what it is.'

16 Eileen
Ann Packman

17

18

19

20

21 _____

_____

22 _____

_____

23 _____

_____

24 _____

_____

_____

25 _____

_____

26 _____

_____

27 _____

28 _____

29 _____

30 _____

He climbed to the top of his tree and climbed down
again, and then he wondered what Pooh was doing, and
went across the Forest to see.

OCTOBER

1 _____

_____

2 _____

_____

3 _____

_____

4

5

6

7

8

9

10

11

12 _____

_____

_____

13 _____

_____

'Now,' said Rabbit, 'this is a Search, and I've Organized it. Which means – well, it's what you do to a Search, when you don't all look in the same place at once.'

14 _____

_____

_____

15 _____

_____

_____

16 _____

_____

_____

17 _____

_____

18 _____

_____

19 _____

_____

20 _____

_____

_____

21 _____

_____

_____

22 _____

_____

_____

23 _____

_____

_____

'Come on, it's easy!' squeaked Roo.
And suddenly Tigger found how easy it was.
'Ow!' he shouted as the tree flew past him.
'Look out!' cried Christopher Robin to the others.

24 _____

_____

_____

25 _____

_____

26 _____

_____

27 _____

_____

28 _____

_____

_____

29 _____

_____

30 _____

_____

31 _____

_____

'I think we're in a sort of Pit. I was
walking along, looking for
somebody, and then suddenly I
wasn't any more, and just when I got
up to see where I was, something fell
on me. And it was you.'

'Nearly eleven o'clock,' said Pooh happily. 'You're just in time for a little smackerel of something,' and he put his head into the cupboard. 'And then we'll go out, Piglet, and sing my song to Eeyore.'

NOVEMBER

1

2

3

4   Alex 1993

5

6

7

8   Graeme

9 _____

_____

10 _____

_____

11 _____

_____

12 _____

_____

13 _____

_____

14 _____

_____

15 _____

_____

16 _____

_____

17 _____

_____

18 _____

_____

19 _____

_____

20 _____

_____

'It's a funny thing,' said Rabbit ten minutes later,
'how everything looks the same in a mist. Have you
noticed it, Pooh?'

21 Anthony

22

23

24

25

26 _____

_____

27 _____

_____

28 _____

_____

29 _____

_____

30 _____

_____

The Piglet lived in a very grand house in the middle of a
beech-tree, and the beech-tree was in the middle of the
Forest, and the Piglet lived in the middle of the house.

DECEMBER

1 _____

2 _____

3 _____

4 _____

_____

_____

5 _____

_____

6 _____

_____

7 _____

_____

8 _____

_____

9 _____

_____

10 _____

_____

11 _____

_____

12 _____

_____

13 _____

14 _____

_____

15 _____

_____

16 _____

_____

So Whatever-it-was came here, and in the light of the candle he and Pooh looked at each other.

17 _____

_____

18 _____

_____

19 _____

_____

20 _____

_____

21 _____

_____

22 _____

_____

23 _____

_____

24 _____

_____

_____

25 _____

_____

_____

26 _____

_____

'When you wake up in the morning, Pooh,' said
Piglet at last, 'what's the first thing you say to yourself?'
'What's for breakfast?' said Pooh.
'What do *you* say, Piglet?'

27 _____

_____

_____

28 _____

_____

_____

29 _____

_____

_____

30 _____

_____

_____

31 _____

_____

_____

. . . and in a moment I heard Winnie-the-Pooh – *bump*, *bump*, *bump* – going up the stairs behind him.